50 NIFTY
CARD TRICKS
& GAMES

Written by Sheryl Scarborough
Illustrated by Neal Yamamoto

Lowell House
Juvenile

NTC Publishing Group

Viva Books Private Limited

NOTE: The numbered card in the upper right-hand corner of each game indicates the level of difficulty; 1 being the easiest, 3 being the hardest.

"WHAT YOU'LL NEED" NOTE: All you need for most of the games and tricks is one deck of regular playing cards, the jokers removed, and a table or floor to play on. If a game or trick needs anything more or something different, it is stated under "WHAT YOU'LL NEED."

Published by Lowell House
A division of NTC/Contemporary Publishing Group, Inc.
4255 West Touhy Avenue, Lincolnwood (Chicago)
Illinois 60646-1975 U.S.A.

Copyright © 1995 by RGA Publishing Group, Inc.

First South Asian Edition 1999

ISBN 1-56565-221-5

Library of Congress Catalog Card Number: 94-41286

Printed and bound at Replika Press Pvt Ltd, 100% EOU
Delhi 110 040, India

INTRODUCTION

Before you shuffle up some fun, here are a few things you need to know:

BOOK: A group of four cards that have the same value is known as a book. Four sevens are a book of sevens; four tens are a book of tens.

CARDS: There are fifty-two cards in a regular deck. These cards are divided into four different suits: clubs, spades, hearts, and diamonds. There are thirteen cards in each suit. The cards, in order from high to low, are ace, king, queen, jack, ten, nine, eight, seven, six, five, four, three, and two.

DEAL and DEALER: To deal means to pass out the correct number of cards to each player. A dealer normally passes out one card at a time, face down, around the circle clockwise, then deals to himself or herself last. After each hand, the next player in the circle becomes the dealer, so everyone gets a chance to deal.

FACE CARD: Face cards have a picture of a person on them. The face cards are the king, queen, and jack.

FACE UP or FACE DOWN: This is an instruction for how to deal or play the cards. Face up means that the front of the cards show. Face down means that the back design of the cards show.

HAND: The cards dealt to you in a game are called a hand.

PAIR: Any two cards that share the same number or face card are a pair, such as the two of hearts and the two of diamonds, or the queen of spades and the queen of diamonds.

WILD CARD: This special card beats the high card in a game. The wild card varies, depending on the game.

1 SLAP HAPPY

Who has the quickest reflexes? Find out in this fast-moving game that really *jacks* up the fun!

WHAT YOU'LL NEED

• two to six players
• paper to keep score on
• pen or pencil

HOW TO PLAY

1 Choose one person to be the dealer. The dealer shuffles the cards and deals out the entire deck, one at a time, face down, to the players.

2 Players pick up their cards but don't look at them.

3 When the dealer says "go," all players turn the top card from their stacks face up into the middle of the circle.

4 Players check the cards quickly. If there is no jack, the dealer says "go" again. Everyone turns over another card. Continue playing until someone turns over a jack.

5 As soon as you spot a jack, slap your hands twice over your head, then slap the jack. The first player to slap the jack gets to pick up all the cards in the middle and set them face down in a pile in front of him or her.

6 Keep playing until all four jacks in the deck have appeared. The player who slaps the last jack not only gets the middle cards but also collects all the cards from the other players' stacks.

7 Players count up the number of cards they've won. The dealer writes down the scores on a piece of paper. The person with the highest score at the end of three games is the winner.

2 COLOR CHANGE-O

Amaze and astound your friends into believing you can change the color of the cards in a deck by simply blowing on them.

WHAT YOU'LL NEED

• deck of cards with a joker

HOW TO DO IT

PLACE EACH BLACK CARD ABOUT ¼ INCH BELOW THE TOP OF THE RED CARD.

FLIPPING ONE END OF THE DECK SHOWS ONLY THE RED CARDS...

...FLIPPING THE OTHER END SHOWS ONLY THE BLACK ONES.

1 In order to make the trick work, prepare your cards in advance when no one is looking. Arrange the entire deck of cards in alternating colors: one red, one black, one red, one black, and so on. Place each black card about ¼ inch below the top of each red card. Now place the joker on top so no one will be able to see the final black card. Turn the deck over so that the back design is showing.

2 Find a friend or family member to be your audience. You are now ready to demonstrate your trick.

3 Tell your audience, "First, let me show you the deck. It is entirely made out of red cards." Carefully grip the bottom of the cards in your right hand, so no one will see that the cards are staggered. Firmly run your left thumb through the tops of the cards, and only the red cards will show.

4 Now say to your audience, "I can change the color of these cards simply by blowing on them." Turn the cards upside down, and grasp the bottom of the deck by your left hand. Blow on the deck of cards. Then firmly run your right thumb through the tops of the cards, and only the black cards show.

5 For the grand finale, tell your audience, "Now I will mix up the colors of the cards simply by blowing on them." First, quickly tap the cards with your fingers. This will make all the cards line up together and mix up the colors. Then blow on the deck for effect. Flip through the stack with your thumb, and the colors will now be mixed, red and black together!

5

3 GO FISH

Hook up pairs of cards in this game that's even more fun than fishing. The best part is you won't have to touch any worms!

WHAT YOU'LL NEED

• two to five players

HOW TO PLAY

1 Choose one person to be the dealer. Before the dealer shuffles, he or she removes one card from the middle of the deck and sets it aside without looking at it. This is called the "shark." The dealer then shuffles the cards and passes out seven cards to each player, one at a time, face down.

2 The dealer next places the leftover cards face down in a stack in the center of the circle. These cards are called the "fishpond." The dealer then takes one card from the fishpond and places it face up next to the fishpond. This is the throw-away pile.

3 Players hold their cards in a fan shape and arrange them by pairs.

4 Players remove any pairs from their hands and place them face down in front of them.

5 The person to the left of the dealer goes first. He or she goes on a "fishing expedition" to find cards that will make pairs with the cards in his or her hand. To do this, he or she asks one of the other players for a needed card. For example, if the first player has a six and wants to make a pair, he or she asks any one person of his or her choice, "Do you have any sixes?" If that player does, he or she has to give it to the first player. The first player then lays down the pair face down in front of him or her and continues asking other players for cards until he or she can't make a pair. If the player asked doesn't have the card requested, he or she says, "Go fish." The first player must then go to the fishpond, take the top card, and add it to his or her hand.

6 If the card from the pond allows the player to make a pair, the player continues asking other players for cards, until he or she can't make a pair.

7 At any time during his or her turn, if a player has a card he or she can't find a pair for, he or she can say, "I think I have the matching shark." Remember, the shark card was the one card the dealer laid aside in the beginning of the game. The dealer turns over the shark, and if the player is right, he or she wins the game! But if the player is wrong, he or she loses a turn.

8 Then, the next player "goes fishing." Players keep taking turns until someone is completely out of cards. Everyone counts his or her pairs. The player with the most pairs is the winner. If all the cards in the fishpond are used before someone runs out of cards, the dealer turns the throw-away pile over, shuffles the cards, and starts a new fishpond with them.

4 WILD ROAR

This is the purr-fect game to bring out your animal instincts!

WHAT YOU'LL NEED

• four to six players

HOW TO PLAY

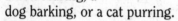

1 Each player picks an animal and imitates its sound, such as a lion roaring, a dog barking, or a cat purring.

2 Choose one person to be the dealer. The dealer shuffles the cards and deals out the entire deck, one at a time, face down, to the players.

3 Players pick up their stacks of cards but don't look at them.

4 The player to the left of the dealer goes first and turns face up his or her top card, placing it in front of him or her. One by one, each player around the circle also turns up a card and places it in front of him or her.

5 Players keep turning cards onto their own face-up stack until there is a pair. The first player to notice the pair AND make the sound of his or her animal wins both stacks of cards belonging to the two players with the pair. The winner places the two stacks under his or her playing stack.

6 Play until one person has all the cards. He or she is the winner. If you want to end the game before someone has all the cards, have each player count up his or her cards. The player with the most cards wins.

TO MAKE IT TOUGHER: Change the rules so that when a player notices a pair of cards on the table, he or she has to make the animal sounds of both players who played those cards.

5 BOTTOMS UP!

Your friends will never get to the bottom of this easy but impressive trick!

WHAT YOU'LL NEED

TOP

BOTTOM

• deck of regular playing cards with a picture on the back that has a top and a bottom

HOW TO DO IT

1 Arrange the entire deck of cards so all the tops point in the same direction.

2 Next, approach an unsuspecting friend or family member and tell him or her you can guess what card he or she picks out of the deck.

3 Position the cards in your hand so the bottom of the design is pointing toward your body. Arrange the cards into the shape of a fan, and allow your friend to choose one card and look at it without showing you what it is.

4 While your friend is looking at the card, casually de-fan the cards and turn the pack around so that the top of the design is now pointing toward your body. Ask your friend to replace the card into the middle of the deck. This card will now be the only one with an upside-down back design.

5 Then flip through the cards one at a time. Tell your friend that the chosen card gives off certain vibes that only you can feel. Actually, you are looking for the one upside-down card. When you find it, pull it out and show it to your friend. He or she will be amazed at what a "card" you are at magic tricks!

9

6 BLACK-ON-RED SOLITAIRE

• •

This twist on the traditional game of solitaire is guaranteed to bring you hours of solo fun.

HOW TO PLAY

1 Sit at a table with enough room to spread out your cards. Then shuffle the cards.

2 First, set up the cards. Start by laying out a horizontal line of seven cards in front of you. Put the first six cards FACE DOWN, from left to right. Turn the seventh, or last card, FACE UP. Cover the first line of cards, starting from the left, with five cards FACE DOWN. Turn the sixth card FACE UP. Cover this line of cards, again starting from the left, with four cards FACE DOWN. Turn the fifth card FACE UP. Cover this line of cards with three cards FACE DOWN. Turn the fourth card FACE UP. Cover this line of cards with two cards FACE DOWN. Turn the third card FACE UP. Cover this line of cards with one card FACE DOWN and one card FACE UP. And finally, on the left-hand stack place a single card FACE UP. Set aside the rest of the cards. You will use them later.

3 The object of the game is to move the cards from this line to four separate piles, in order, from the highest card (ace), to the lowest card (two), alternating colors (black and red).

4 To start, if any aces are showing, remove them and place each one separately above the row. If possible, place any face-up cards on aces above, starting with the king, alternating black and red. Otherwise, to uncover more face-down cards, play the face-up cards on each other by moving higher cards to lower cards, alternating black and red. For example, move a black nine to a red eight, and a red jack to a black ten. Following this rule, move as many cards as possible, each time turning up the next face-down card and trying to play those cards as well. If you turn over an ace, put the ace above. If you turn over a king, place it on the appropriate ace (black on red or red on black).

5 When you can move no other cards, pick up the stack of leftover cards. Count out three cards and turn them face up. If you can play the top card, do so. Then you're free to play the second or third card if possible. When you have no more plays, turn up three more cards and repeat.

6 Move up lines of cards to the aces as soon as you can. Keep playing and moving cards until you have moved all the cards possible from the line up to the new stacks of aces, with the cards all in order, alternating black and red.

7 If you move all of the cards from the line to their appropriate place on the ace stacks, you win. If you aren't able to move all of your cards, play again and see if the second time's a charm!

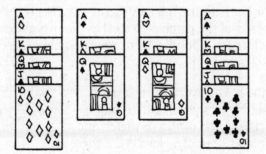

7 IT TAKES A THIEF

Here's a game where you can steal your opponents' cards right out from under their noses!

WHAT YOU'LL NEED

• two to four players

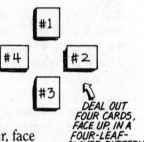

DEAL OUT FOUR CARDS, FACE UP, IN A FOUR-LEAF-CLOVER PATTERN.

HOW TO PLAY

1 Choose one person to be the dealer. The dealer shuffles the cards and deals four cards to each player, face down. Next, he or she deals four cards face up in the center, in a four-leaf-clover pattern. Each card in the center is called a bundle.

2 The person sitting to the left of the dealer goes first. If that player has a card in his or her hand that makes a pair with the top card of any bundle, the player takes the card from his or her hand and places it on the bundle face up. The player then picks up the bundle and places it in front of him or her with the top card facing up. This is called "stealing" a bundle. The object of the game is to steal as many bundles as possible. If the player can't match a bundle, he or she must choose a card from his or her hand to discard.

3 Now it's the next player's turn to try to match a bundle. He or she can either match and steal a bundle in the center or match and steal another player's bundle. However, if there are fewer than four bundles on the table at any time, the player must use his or her turn to place a card in the empty space, creating a new bundle. There must always be four bundles in the middle of the table.

4 Go around the circle, with each player trying to steal a bundle. When players run out of cards in their hand, they ask the dealer to give them four more cards from the unused stack and continue playing.

5 After all the cards have been played, the game is over. Players count their cards. The player with the most cards wins.

STACK THEM UP!

This impressive card trick really stacks the deck in your favor, and it works every time!

HOW TO DO IT

1 With your audience watching, lay out twenty-one cards, face up, into three stacks, one card at a time to each stack. Overlap the cards so your audience can see all seven cards in each stack. Set the rest of the deck aside—you don't need it.

2 Ask a volunteer in your audience to mentally choose any card from one of the stacks and remember it. Next, ask your friend which stack the card is in. Tell the friend, "Just by knowing which stack the chosen card is in, I will find it."

3 Pile the stacks on top of each other so that the stack containing the selected card is in between the other two stacks.

4 Lay the cards out again, face up, into three stacks of seven. Ask the volunteer to again tell you which stack the card is in.

5 Restack the cards, placing the selected stack in the middle between the other two stacks, and again lay them out in the same manner as Step 1.

6 Ask the volunteer to tell you for the last time which stack the chosen card is in. Because of the way you laid out and stacked the cards, the chosen card will be the fourth (or middle) card in the stack the volunteer pointed to. Pull out the card and show it to your volunteer. Who is more surprised at your magician's skill—you or your audience?

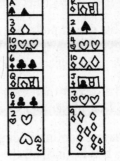

13

9 MAID FOR A DAY

Old Maid like you've never seen her before! Play it with your family, and make a deal that the loser has to do all of the chores for a day!

WHAT YOU'LL NEED

• two to six players

HOW TO PLAY

1 Choose one person to be the dealer. Ask the dealer to remove the queen of clubs from the deck, because you won't be needing it. The dealer then shuffles the cards and deals them all out, one at a time, face down, to the players. (It doesn't matter if a player or two has one card more than the others.)

2 Players check their cards to see if they have any pairs of the same color—for example, a three of hearts and a three of diamonds. Each player removes all same-color pairs and places them face down in front of him or her.

3 The player to the left of the dealer goes first by arranging his or her cards in a fan shape so they can't be seen by the other players. This player then offers the cards to the player on the left.

4 That player picks one card out of the first player's hand and places it into his or her own hand. If this card makes a same-color pair, the player removes it and places it face down in front of him or her.

5 That player then offers his or her hand to the next player around the circle. That player picks a card and removes any same-color pairs.

6 Players continue going around the circle, picking cards from each other's hands, until all the cards are paired up, except for one, the queen of spades. The person left holding the queen of spades loses, and is "maid for the day"!

STRATEGY ALERT: If you get the queen of spades, play it cool and don't give it away by sighing or rolling your eyes. The game is a lot more fun when no one knows who has the deadly queen.

10 THE VANISHING CARD

Your audience will never disappear on you while you demonstrate this exciting trick that makes a card vanish before their very eyes.

WHAT YOU'LL NEED

• handkerchief
• regular wooden toothpick

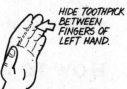

HIDE TOOTHPICK BETWEEN FINGERS OF LEFT HAND.

HOW TO DO IT

1 Before you begin this trick, put the toothpick between your index and middle fingers in your left hand so it can't be seen. Place the handkerchief on the table.

2 Put the deck of cards into a pile on a table in front of your audience. With your right hand, pick up the handkerchief and shake it out to show there is nothing inside.

3 Reach for the pile of cards with your left hand. Throw the handkerchief over your left hand. Tell your audience that you will lift up one card *inside* the handkerchief.

INSTEAD OF PICKING UP CARD, GRASP TOOTHPICK ACROSS THE TOP...

4 Instead of picking up a card, roll the toothpick off your fingers and into the top of the handkerchief with your left hand. With your right hand, grasp the toothpick between your thumb and forefinger, and slowly lift the handkerchief up from the table. The toothpick inside the handkerchief will look as if you are holding a card. Wave your left hand over the handkerchief and say, "Abracadabra!"

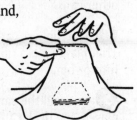

5 With your thumb and fingers of your left hand, grab a bottom corner of the handkerchief and yank it across your body to the left. At the same time, let go of the toothpick. If you do this quickly, and with a large, sweeping movement, no one will notice the toothpick as it drops onto the floor. It will look as if you made the card disappear in thin air!

STRATEGY ALERT: This trick may work better for you if you switch your left and right hands in the instructions above.

11 THE SECRET SPOILER

This card game is the best secret in town—share it with your friends!

WHAT YOU'LL NEED

- two to six players
- extra deck of regular playing cards

HOW TO PLAY

1 Choose one person to be the dealer. The dealer shuffles the cards and deals out the entire deck, one at a time, to the players. (Each player should have the same number of cards. Leftover cards can be set aside for that hand, then reshuffled into the deck for the next hand.)

2 Players arrange their cards by suits. Before play begins, the dealer pulls one card from the middle of the extra deck of cards and sets it aside without looking at it. No one else should look at it either. This card is called the "secret spoiler."

3 The player to the left of the dealer goes first by laying any card of his or her choice into the middle of the circle. Whatever suit the first player puts down is called the leading suit. The other players must play cards from the leading suit. If they don't have one, they can play any other card.

4 The highest card in the leading suit wins the cards for that round. That player picks up the cards and places them face down in front of him or her.

5 Once all the cards have been played, the dealer turns up the secret spoiler card. Now all the players look through their cards and pull out any that match the *suit* or *number* of the secret spoiler.

6 Each player counts one point for each suit that matches the spoiler card and ten points for each number that matches the spoiler card. The person with the *highest* number of points *loses*. You can play from 50 to 500, whatever you have time for.

12 SWITCH-ER-OO

Here's a switch for you—in this game, the ace is low instead of being high. Winners keep playing while losers drop out, until there is only one person left.

WHAT YOU'LL NEED

• six to ten players

HOW TO PLAY

1 Choose one person to be the dealer. The dealer shuffles the cards and deals one card face down to each player. Players look at their cards.

2 The player to the left of the dealer goes first. He or she has a choice to either keep the card if the card seems high (kings are the highest) or get a new one if it's on the low side (aces are the lowest). To change cards, the player says, "Switch-er-oo." The player on his or her *right* must switch cards with the first player, unless he or she is holding the highest card, a king. That player must show the king to all the players in order to keep it.

3 Continue around the circle, with each player taking a turn deciding whether to keep or switch cards.

4 After everyone has had a turn, all players lay down their cards, face up, in the center at the same time. The person with the lowest card must drop out of this game (remember, aces are low). If two or more players have the same low card, this is considered a tie, and no one drops out.

5 The dealer collects the cards from the middle and sets them aside, then deals another round of cards to the remaining players.

6 Continue playing until only one player is left in the game. He or she is the winner. If you run out of cards before there is a winner, the dealer may shuffle the used cards and start again.

13 SPELLBINDING

In this trick, you use an index card to help spell out a friend's chosen card. Can you spell C-O-O-L T-R-I-C-K?

WHAT YOU'LL NEED

• pencil or pen
• 3-by-5-inch index card
• scissors

HOW TO DO IT

1 Use the scissors to cut the index card so that it is ½ inch smaller than a card from your deck. Set this aside until later.

2 Grab a friend from the audience. Explain that in this trick you're going to magically be able to find a certain card in the deck that only the friend has seen.

3 Next, pick up the deck of cards, saying you want to make sure there are no jokers in this deck. This will give you a chance to go through the cards without your friend knowing what you're doing. Turn the deck of cards over so the cards are face up. As you look through the cards, count the cards until you reach the twelfth card. Don't let your friend know you're counting. Remember the number and face of this twelfth card. Put the cards down.

4 Tell your friend that before he or she chooses a card, you're going to make a prediction about which card he or she will choose. Take the index card and tell your friend you're writing down your prediction. But instead write, "THIS MUST BE IT." Don't let your friend see what you've written.

PLACE THE INDEX CARD BEHIND THE TWELFTH CARD...

●●

5 Pick up the deck and fan the cards until you see the twelfth card. Put the index card behind the twelfth card, making it the thirteenth card. Don't let your friend see that you're counting cards; simply tell him or her, "Now I will put this index card randomly back in the deck."

6 Square up the deck and place it face down, so that the thirteen cards are now on the bottom.

7 Hand the deck to your friend. Ask him or her to pick up a stack of cards from the top of the deck. Tell him or her to pick up *less* than half the deck.

8 Tell your friend to shuffle these cards and to look at the top card and remember it. Then tell him or her to put the card back on top of the deck and give the deck a cut. Again, he or she should pick up less than half of the deck.

9 Take the deck and cut it at the index card. This will be easy, because the index card is not the same size as the playing cards.

10 Set the top stack to one side and place the bottom stack on top. The index card will be on top of the deck. Because of the way you laid out the cards and cut the cards, your friend's remembered card will now be the twelfth card from the top.

11 Give your friend the index card and ask him or her to read it out loud, letter by letter: T-H-I-S M-U-S-T B-E I-T. Tell your friend, "I will turn over one card for each letter you read, plus one for good luck. The last card I turn over will be the card you remembered." Turn over twelve cards, one for each letter. The thirteenth card will be your friend's chosen card, just as you predicted!

14 · CARD-INGO

You'll be calling out for more when you play this card version of bingo!

WHAT YOU'LL NEED

• three to six players
• second deck of regular playing cards

HOW TO PLAY

1 Choose one player to act as the dealer. This person will not play the game. The dealer then shuffles the cards and deals seven cards, one at a time, face up, to each player.

2 Players lay their cards face up on the table in front of them, so all of the cards are showing.

3 The dealer takes the second deck of cards and turns over one card at a time, calling out the number and suit. If a player's card matches the card called out, the player turns his or her card face down. The first person to turn over all cards yells out, "Card-ingo!" and wins the game.

STRATEGY ALERT: Be sure to pay attention to the dealer. If you don't hear a card when it is called, you're not allowed to ask the dealer to call it again.

15 SEVEN UP

This game where you build on sevens to get rid of all of your cards will put you in seventh heaven!

WHAT YOU'LL NEED

• three to eight players

HOW TO PLAY

1 Choose someone to be the dealer. The dealer shuffles the cards and deals out the entire deck, one at a time, face down, to the players. (It doesn't matter if a player or two has one card more than the others.)

2 Players look at their hands and arrange the cards in the shape of a fan.

3 The first card played must be a seven. The player to the left of the dealer goes first. If that player is holding a seven, he or she lays it in the center of the table. If that player doesn't have a seven, he or she must pass, and the next person in the circle gets a chance to play a seven.

4 Once the first seven has been played, the next player can build on that seven by adding a card that is higher or lower in the same suit. For example, if the next player has a six in the same suit, he or she places the six to the left of the seven so the cards overlap. If the player has an eight, he or she places the eight to the right of the seven. Or, if the person has another seven, he or she starts a new line by placing it above or below the first seven. If the player doesn't have a card that can be played, he or she passes.

5 The next player takes a turn. Continue around the circle, with each player taking a turn building on any of the cards, adding one higher or lower card in the same suit.

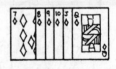

6 Keep playing until one player is out of cards. That player is the winner!

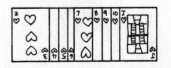

21

16 DROP AND SNATCH

This trick where you appear to grab a preselected card out of midair will make you look like an old hand at card tricks.

WHAT YOU'LL NEED

• roll of double-sided clear tape

HOW TO DO IT

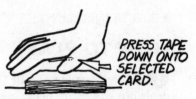

PRESS TAPE DOWN ONTO SELECTED CARD.

1 When no one is looking, slip a small piece of double-sided tape into the palm of your right hand. Set the deck of cards on the table in front of you, face down. With your left hand, pull a card from the middle of the deck and show it to your audience. Make sure everyone knows which card this is.

2 Place this card on top of the deck. Use your right hand (with the tape) to pick up the top half of the deck, and move it to your right. Keep your right hand over the top of these cards.

3 Now tell your audience, "In a few seconds, I will pluck this chosen card out of midair." Pick up the left stack of cards with your left hand, and throw the cards up into the air. While your audience is distracted by the thrown cards, press your right hand down onto the top card, sticking it to the tape and to your hand. Quickly bring your right hand up and appear to snatch the card out of midair. Show the card around so everyone gets a chance to see it.

17 HEART ATTACK

You'll be more than happy to give your heart away in this classic game of hearts!

WHAT YOU'LL NEED

• two to six players

HOW TO PLAY

1 Choose one person to be the dealer. The dealer shuffles the cards and deals out the entire deck, one at a time, face down, to the players. (Each player should have the same number of cards. Leftover cards can be set aside for that hand, then reshuffled into the deck for the next hand.) Players pick up their cards and arrange them in a fan shape in their hands.

2 The goal of this game is to win as few hearts as possible. The player to the left of the dealer plays first. He or she lays down one card and places it in the middle playing area. All other players follow in order, playing a card from their hand that matches the suit. If a player doesn't have a card in that suit, he or she *must* play a heart. If that player has neither a heart nor a card in that suit, he or she can play any card. The person with the highest card *in the suit originally played* wins the cards in that round, called a trick, and stacks them in front of him or her.

3 The person to the left of the first player begins the second round, laying down a card from his or her hand, with other players following suit. Again, the person with the highest card *in the suit originally played* at the beginning of the second round wins that hand.

4 Continue playing until all the cards have been played. Then players count up how many heart cards they have in their tricks. The person with the least number of hearts is the winner.

STRATEGY ALERT: Because the goal of the game is to win as few hearts as possible, try to avoid playing high cards in the leading suit whenever hearts are played. Also, get rid of any high hearts you're holding by playing them whenever you can't match the starting player's suit.

18 ◇ FACE CARD FACE-OFF

Use the kings, queens, and jacks to help you find a chosen card.

HOW TO DO IT

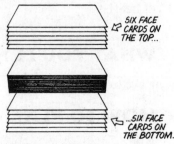

SIX FACE CARDS ON THE TOP...

...SIX FACE CARDS ON THE BOTTOM.

1 To make the trick work, you'll need to set up the cards in a certain way when no one is looking. First, remove all the face cards—the kings, queens, and jacks. Place six face cards face down on the bottom of the deck and six face cards face down on the top of the deck. It doesn't matter in which order you put them. Next, remove four cards from the middle of the deck—it doesn't matter which ones—and put them aside. For this trick to work, the deck must have only forty-eight cards.

2 Now grab an audience. Lay out the forty-eight cards into six equal piles, face down, one card at a time to each pile. Because of the way you set up the deck, every pile will have a *face card* on the top and a *face card* on the bottom. You don't have to check, they'll just be there.

3 Tell your audience, "I'm going to leave the room. While I'm gone, someone pick a stack and remove a card from the middle of that stack. When you have all seen the card, place it face down on top of the pile it came from. Restack the cards in any order you wish." Then leave the room for a few minutes.

4 When you return, tell your audience, "Now I will find the card you just selected." Look through the deck until you find one *regular* card *in between* two face cards. This is the selected card. Take it out and proudly show it to your admiring audience.

SECRET TO THE TRICK: When your volunteer took a card from a stack, he or she replaced it on the top of the same stack—on top of a face card. And, when he or she stacked the piles together, the bottom card of the stack that went on top was also a face card, thus "surrounding" the chosen card.

LOOK FOR THE ONE REGULAR CARD BETWEEN TWO FACE CARDS.

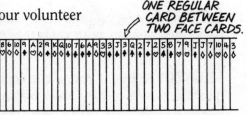

19 "THAT'S NOT SO, JOE!"

This game is for players who can bluff their way out of anything—even a bad hand!

WHAT YOU'LL NEED

• four to five players

HOW TO PLAY

1 Choose one person to be the dealer. The dealer shuffles the cards and deals out the entire deck, one by one, face down, to the players. (It doesn't matter if a player or two has one card more than the others.) Players arrange their cards in a fan, keeping them hidden from the other players.

2 The goal of this game is to get rid of all of your cards as quickly as possible, in order from the highest to the lowest. The player to the left of the dealer goes first, by removing any aces from his or her hand and putting them face down in the middle of the playing area. The player must also announce how many aces he or she is putting down. If the player doesn't have any aces, he or she can do one of two things: (1) pass or (2) bluff and try to get rid of cards by putting down ones that aren't aces. If, however, another player suspects the first player is bluffing, he or she says, "That's not so, Joe." The first player must then turn over the cards and reveal if they are aces or not. If the player was bluffing, he or she has to pick up the "bluffing" cards and put them back in his or her hand. If the player was telling the truth, the other player has to pick up all the cards.

3 If no one accuses the first player of bluffing, then all the other players discard their aces (if they have any) onto the top of the pile. Only the first player in each round can bluff.

4 In the second round, everyone removes any kings from his or her hand. The first player to put down kings has the choice to bluff or not. In the third round, queens are removed, then jacks, tens, and so on, until all the cards, down to the twos, have been played.

5 If no player has managed to get rid of all of his or her cards, players start back with aces and continue playing until one person is out of cards. This person is the winner. If you have to stop the game before one person is out of cards, have each player count up his or her stack of cards. The person with the least number of cards is the winner.

20 RAISE THE ROOF

Do you have the gentle touch it takes to build a delicate house of cards? Find out in this true test of skill that lays the foundation for many hours of fun.

WHAT YOU'LL NEED

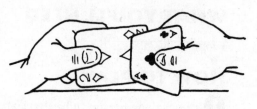

• one to four players
• table with a large, flat surface

HOW TO PLAY

❶ The first person takes two cards and turns them lengthwise. He or she places them on a table and pushes them together to make a corner, holding the cards steady until they balance against each other. The player then carefully removes his or her hands. The two cards will stand on their own.

❷ The next player adds two more cards, forming a square.

❸ Players continue to take turns, adding two cards at a time. Players can either make new squares or lay two cards on top of a square to create a roof. Once a roof is made, players can add another square, or "second story," on the roof.

❹ Continue taking turns until one player crashes all or part of the house. Then pick up all the cards, and start building again.

❺ The first player to crash the house three times is the loser.

STRATEGY NOTE: Be patient. It can take a few tries before you get the hang of building card houses. But with a little practice, you'll find yourselves getting better and better and building larger and larger structures.

21 ON EDGE

Your friends will stand back in awe when you make an ordinary card stand up on end by itself!

HOW TO DO IT

1 Grab an audience. Take the top card off the pack of playing cards and place it vertically in your hand.

2 While doing this, keep a little conversation going with your audience. Say something like: "This card is the most amazing card in the deck. It can do a very special trick. It can stand all on its own." Then pretend to talk to the card, saying, "Are you ready, card? Everyone is watching you." You only want to talk long enough to get the interest of your audience and to give you some time to set up the trick.

3 While talking, give the card a good squeeze so that the sides slightly bend forward toward each other. The bend will be so slight that no one will probably notice it.

4 Set the bottom of the card on a table and balance it. The slight bend you've given the card is just enough to keep the card standing. Gently pull your hand away. Voilà! It works just like magic!

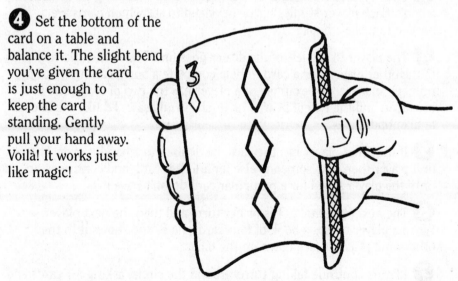

22 SEEK 'N' STEAL

All you have to do is ask the right questions and winning this game will be a real steal!

WHAT YOU'LL NEED

• three to six players

HOW TO PLAY

1 Choose one person to be the dealer. The dealer shuffles the cards and deals out the entire deck, one at a time, face down, to the players. (It doesn't matter if a player or two has one card more than the others.)

2 Each player arranges his or her cards in a fan shape, keeping them hidden, and then arranges them according to sets. A set is a group of matching cards, such as three twos or two kings.

3 The object of this game is to collect all four matching cards to make a book. Each player studies his or her hand to see which cards are needed to make a book.

4 The player to the left of the dealer goes first. He or she asks any one of the other players for a card to help complete a book, calling it out by number and suit. For example, if a player has the two of clubs, the two of spades, and the two of hearts, he or she would say, "I'd like the two of diamonds."

5 If the other player has the card, he or she must hand it over. The first player then asks someone else for another card, and continues on until the player asked for a particular card doesn't have it.

6 The next player takes his or her turn, and then the next player. When a player makes a book of four cards, he or she shows it to the others and places it face down on the table.

7 Players continue taking turns around the circle, asking for cards and making books. Once someone runs out of cards in his or her hand, players count up their books. The player who has the most books wins the game—and earns the reputation for being the sneakiest card thief!

23 HIT THE DECK

This fast-moving party game is sure to be a hit at your next get-together!

WHAT YOU'LL NEED

- six to twenty players
- second deck of regular playing cards, jokers removed
- two shoe boxes

HOW TO PLAY

1 Divide the players into two equal teams. If you have an extra person, that person can act as the judge. If you have an equal number of players, ask your mom or dad to fill in as judge.

2 Have one person put a deck of cards into each shoe box and shake the boxes well to mix up all the cards.

3 Place the boxes side by side on the floor against a wall, about two feet away from each other.

4 One team lines up ten feet away in front of one box. The other team lines up ten feet away in front of the other box.

5 When the judge says "go," the first member of each team races for his or her team's shoe box. When players reach the box, they flip through the cards until they find a king *of any suit*. With a king in hand, they must race back to where the team is lined up and place the king on the floor next to their line.

6 As soon as a player slaps a king on the floor, the second person in line races to the box and looks for a queen *of the same suit*. The person then runs back to the line and places the queen next to the king. The next person then runs to the box to find a jack that matches the suit of the king and queen.

7 Play continues until one team has found an entire suit of cards in order from king, queen, jack, and ten, down to three, two, and finally the ace. The first team to find the cards in order wins.

24 MYSTERY OF THE MAGIC SYMBOL

Astonish your friends when you use an ancient magic symbol to help you see through a card.

WHAT YOU'LL NEED

• pen or pencil

HOW TO DO IT

1 Grab a friend or family member to be your audience.

2 Tell your friend, "I've discovered an ancient symbol that gives me X-ray vision. If I write down the symbol on the face of a card, I will have X-ray vision and be able to see through the card."

3 To demonstrate, hold the deck in the hand you do not write with. Turn the top card face up and place it on top of the deck, about ½ inch lower than the deck.

4 Draw a symbol of your choice in the middle of the face of the card with a pen or pencil. Afterward, quickly place a tiny dot on the top border of the back of the card behind the card you have drawn the symbol on. Make sure no one sees you draw the dot. Your friend will think that the symbol itself will help you find this marked card. But in reality, you'll use the dot to find the card.

AFTER DRAWING THE MYSTICAL SYMBOL ON THE CARD FACE, SECRETLY PLACE A TINY DOT ON THE TOP BORDER OF THE NEXT CARD.

5 Push up the top card so it is no longer lower than the rest of the deck. This will hide the dot. Hold the card with the symbol out to your friend. Now turn the marked card face down on top of the deck. Hand the deck to your friend.

6 Tell your friend to deal off about half the deck, one card at a time, into a heap on the table. He or she will bury the marked card on the bottom. Take back the remaining deck and place the heap of cards on top.

7 Slowly turn over one card at a time into a pile. When you get to the card with the dot on the back of the card, stop as if you're concentrating for a second, then turn over the card. Tell your friend, "I am able to see through this next card. It is the card with the symbol."

8 Turn the card over and hand the card with the symbol to your friend. He or she will be amazed by your incredible X-ray vision!

25 GO BOOM!

In this tension-packed game, you try to get rid of all your cards as quickly as possible. It's so exciting, you'll feel like you're sitting on a time bomb that's about to go off.

WHAT YOU'LL NEED

- two to four players
- pen and paper for scoring

HOW TO PLAY

1 Choose one person to be the dealer. The dealer hands out seven cards to each player, one at a time, face down. The dealer places the leftover cards in the middle, called the stockpile.

2 Players arrange their cards in a fan shape, keeping others from seeing their hand. The player to the left of the dealer goes first by taking any card from his or her hand and laying it next to the stockpile, face up. This is the "lead card."

3 If the second player has a card that matches either the number or suit of the lead card, he or she lays it down next to the lead card. If not, he or she must draw cards from the stockpile until a match is made.

4 Each player takes a turn making a match. Once everyone has laid out a card, look at the cards that have been played. The person who played the highest card in the *suit* of the lead card has to pick up the stack of cards and add them to his or her hand.

5 The second player now lays down a new lead card. Again, everyone puts down a card in either the same suit or number as the lead card.

6 Continue playing. The first player to get rid of all of his or her cards yells "BOOM!" and is the winner. If you want to keep score, players who still have cards should add up the points left in their hand. The points are:

    aces.. 1
    kings, queens, jacks 10
    all other cards............................numeric value

The person with the lowest total score wins.

26 GOSSIP

If you need an icebreaker for your next party, try this game and you'll have everyone instantly knowing everyone else.

WHAT YOU'LL NEED

• ten to eighteen players

HOW TO PLAY

1 Remove the numbered cards in the suits of hearts and diamonds. You should have a matching pair of hearts and diamonds cards with the same value for every two players. If you have an odd number of guests, you should play. Otherwise, you need to sit out this game. Set all the other cards aside.

2 Mix up the deck, then as the guests come to the door, give each one a card.

3 Tell each guest to find his or her partner, the person with the matching card. For example, the guest with the six of hearts is the partner of the person who has the six of diamonds.

4 Once partners meet, they must share things they love or things they wish for, based on the number and suit of their cards. For instance, a player who has the ten of hearts must tell ten things he or she loves, while a player who has four of diamonds tells his or her four wishes.

5 Gather in a group, and starting with the highest card, the ten, ask each player to stand up and remember at least one thing his or her partner loves or wishes for. Once everyone has shared, take up the cards, hand them out, and play another round with different partners.

ONE STEP FURTHER: You can also play this game with spades (players say things they don't like) and clubs (players list their favorite places to visit).

27 THE TELLTALE TELEPHONE

With this trick that uses a telephone, you may be a phone-y, but your pals will never know it.

WHAT YOU'LL NEED

• friend at another telephone
• your own telephone

HOW TO DO IT

1 First arrange for a friend to phone you at a certain time. Tell this friend to let the phone ring twice, then hang up, call right back and let the phone ring three times, and then hang up for good.

2 About ten minutes before the time scheduled for the call, grab some friends or family members to be your audience. Tell your audience, "In this trick, one of you will choose a card and not show it to me. I am going to use the help of a psychic friend to help me find the card. She (or he) will call on the telephone, and the number of times my friend rings will tell me exactly where your card is."

3 Choose a person in your audience to shuffle the deck. Tell him or her to take off fifteen cards from the top and place them in a pocket or to the side, because you won't be needing them. This trick can only work using thirty-seven cards.

4 Next, tell the person to count off fifteen more cards from the top. Ask the friend to look at and remember the fifteenth card. He or she then replaces the fifteen cards on top of the deck, keeping them in the same order.

5 Ask your friend to begin turning cards over and reading them off, from the top of the deck. After reading each card, he or she is to place each face down on the bottom of the deck. Pretend that you are listening for a certain card. Actually, you are counting the cards being turned over. When your friend turns over the twenty-ninth card, say, "Wait. I'm getting vibes from my friend. She's going to call any minute and tell me which card you selected."

34

6 If you have to kill some time before your friend calls, fill up the time by saying something like, "My psychic friend has never failed to correctly identify a card."

7 Continue talking until the phone rings. It will ring twice, then three times. Turn to your audience and say, "Two rings and three rings. That means the card you chose is the twenty-third card from the top of the deck."

8 Ask the person holding the cards to turn over twenty-three cards. The twenty-third card will be the card he or she chose in the beginning! Your psychic friend was right again!

THE SECRET TO THE TRICK: It's based on a mathematical formula that works due to the number of cards you use (only thirty-seven) and the number of cards you have your friend count off (twenty-nine, then twenty-three). The use of a psychic telephone friend is just a fun way to display the trick.

... YES, MY PSYCHIC POWERS CAN SENSE YOUR THOUGHTS...

 # TWENTY-TWO

Now matter how you count it, this game adds up to a lot of fun—and sometimes even more than one winner.

WHAT YOU'LL NEED

• two to eight players

HOW TO PLAY

1 Choose one person to be the dealer. The dealer shuffles the cards and deals one card to each player, face down. Next, the dealer passes out a second card to each player, face up.

2 The object of the game is to have two cards whose point value is as close to twenty-two without going over twenty-two. The points for cards are: aces can be either two points or twelve points (the choice is up to the player); face cards are ten points; and points for all the other cards are the number on the card.

3 Players study their cards and add up their numbers.

4 The dealer asks the person on the left if that player wants another card. If the player's point total is close to twenty-two, he or she should say, "Stay," which means he or she doesn't want another card. If the player's point total is low, he or she should say, "Hit," which means he or she wants another card.

5 After being "hit" with one card, the player can ask for as many hits as he or she wants. But remember: You don't want to have a point total over twenty-two!

6 The dealer goes around the circle, asking each player if he or she wants more cards.

7 Once everyone has had a turn, players turn their cards face up. The person who has a point total closest to twenty-two without going over is the winner! If more than one player shares the same winning point total, they're all winners.

29 THE RISING CARD

PARENTAL SUPERVISION REQUIRED

You'll get a rise out of your friends when you actually lift cards magically out of the box!

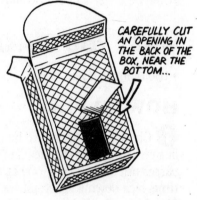

CAREFULLY CUT AN OPENING IN THE BACK OF THE BOX, NEAR THE BOTTOM...

WHAT YOU'LL NEED

- pencil or pen
- scissors
- cardboard box the cards came in

HOW TO DO IT

1 Before you present this trick, you have to prepare the box. Remove the cards from the box. Use the pencil or pen to draw a small square, about ½ inch by ½ inch, on the back of the card box, near the bottom. Ask your parents to use the scissors to carefully cut this square out and throw it away.

2 Replace the cards in the box. Grab a pal to be your audience. To begin the trick, open the box and slide out the cards. Show the cards to your audience, saying, "This is just a normal deck of playing cards. But I can control them whenever I want." Slip the cards back into the box.

PRESS YOUR THUMB THROUGH THE HOLE AND SLIDE THE CARD UP...

3 Hold the box vertically in your left hand with the hole in the back facing you. Keep your fingers on the front of the box and your thumb on the back. Wave your right hand over the box and say a few magic words, such as "presto, change-o." While you are talking, put your thumb over the hole in the box. You will be touching the first card inside. Work your thumb up and down, pressing through the hole. This will slide up the card inside the box, until it sticks out from the top of the box. Abra-card-abra! The card moved without you seeming to touch it!

30 CRAZY ACES

You'd be crazy to pass up playing this old favorite with a new twist!

WHAT YOU'LL NEED

• two to four players

HOW TO PLAY

1 Choose one person to be the dealer. The dealer shuffles and passes out seven cards, one at a time, face down to each player. The dealer then places the leftover cards in the middle, face down. This is called the pickup pile. The dealer turns the top card on the pickup pile face up to start a second pile. This is called the throw-away pile.

2 Players arrange their cards into a fan shape and group the cards according to suit. They also separate out all of the aces and put them together.

3 The object of this game is for each player to match the top card on the throw-away pile with a card from his or her hand. Players can either match the suit or the number of the card. For example, if the top card of the throw-away pile is the five of spades, any spade card or a five in another suit matches. If another five is played, the suit now changes to that of the new card. All four aces are wild. This means you can play an ace on top of any card and choose the suit you want it to be. If a player can't match the suit OR number of the card, he or she must draw from the pick-up pile until he or she finds a card to play.

4 The player to the left of the dealer goes first, finding a card that matches the card on the throw-away pile. Players take turns around the circle.

5 When the pickup pile runs out, the dealer shuffles the throw-away pile and turns it face down to make a new pickup pile. The first person to get rid of all the cards in his or her hand is the winner.

31 DUNK IN THE OCEAN

Dip into this entertaining game where the object is to get rid of your cards as quickly as possible. You and your friends are sure to get along swimmingly!

WHAT YOU'LL NEED

- two to seven players
- regular deck of playing cards for *each* player

HOW TO PLAY

1 Each player shuffles his or her own deck of cards. Each player then lays out five stacks of seven cards face up in front of him or her. Each person sets the leftover cards, the "dunk pile," aside.

2 Together, players say "dunk," and in unison turn up one card from their dunk piles and place them in the center playing area.

3 Players then check the top cards of their five stacks to see if any of them can be played on any of the cards in the middle. Players can play a card in any suit that is either higher or lower than the card in the middle. For example, on

a queen you can play either a king or a jack. On a six you can play either a seven or a five.

4 Players rapidly play as many cards as they can from their stacks.

5 When there are no more cards that can be played, players say "dunk" again and in unison turn up new cards from their dunk piles and place them on top of the cards in the center.

6 Continue playing until one person has played off all of the cards in his or her five stacks. The first person to get rid of his or her cards wins!

32 WHAT A CARD!

You'll stand out from the pack when you make your own deck of playing cards, personalized with your favorite designs and photos.

WHAT YOU'LL NEED

- pencil
- scissors
- glue
- ruler
- large sheet of light-colored construction paper or lightweight cardboard, 22 inches by 28 inches
- stickers—thirteen stickers each of four different symbols (or suits) like rainbows, stars, suns, and clouds (about 2 inches in diameter)
- back design—fifty-two copies of the same design
- marking pens in two to four complementary colors

HOW TO DO IT

1 Using the pencil and ruler, begin by marking a small dot every 2½ inches along both of the *long* edges of the construction paper or cardboard.

2 Next, mark small dots every 3½ inches along both *short* edges of the construction paper. Use the ruler to connect the dots, vertically and horizontally, with a light pencil line. You need at least fifty-two 2½-inch-by-3½-inch rectangles. These pencil lines will be your cutting lines. But don't cut yet.

3 Decide on the back design. If you are using a photograph, you can have it photocopied at a copying facility. Make sure the photo will fit inside the 3½-inch-by-2½-inch card. (To save money on photocopying, make ten copies first. Cut and paste or tape all ten photos to one sheet of paper, then copy that paper five times.)

4 Once you have your fifty-two back designs, glue them inside the penciled rectangles on your sheet. Let glue dry for several hours.

5 Once glue is dry, carefully cut along the pencil lines until you have your fifty-two-card deck. One side will bear your design; the other side should be blank.

6 Separate the cards into four piles of thirteen cards each. Make sure the cards are arranged with all the tops pointing the same way.

7 Now flip the stacks over to show the blank sides of the cards. You are now going to create your suits. Choose one sticker design for each suit and apply one sticker to the middle of each card. Choose two colors of marking pens and begin marking your cards in the upper left-hand corner in the following order: king, queen, jack, ten, nine, eight, seven, six, five, four, three, two, and ace. Turn the cards face down and keep in order after marking. Color two suits in one color and two suits in a different color.

8 Flip the stack over and turn the cards around so that the numbers or letters are on the right-hand side of the cards and appear upside down. Using the same color marking pens, repeat and mark the top left-hand side of the cards exactly as before. When you're finished, you'll have your own deck of personalized cards!

TO MAKE IT TOUGHER: To make your cards last longer, you have the option of having them laminated. Most copying facilities can laminate for a small charge. If you plan to laminate, it is best to design and decorate *both* the front and back of your cards *before* cutting. This way you can have the whole sheet laminated at one time, which is easier and cheaper. (Mark your pencil cutting lines on *both* sides of the paper before decorating. This will ensure that your designs stay within the lines.)

41

33 TRADING PLACES

Your friends will jump at the chance to find out how you make two cards, the eight of hearts and the seven of diamonds, jump from the bottom of the deck to the top.

HOW TO DO IT

1 Before you demonstrate this trick, pull out four cards—eight of hearts, eight of diamonds, seven of hearts, and seven of diamonds—when no one is looking. Place the eight of hearts and the seven of diamonds on the top of the stack. Put the eight of diamonds and the seven of hearts aside.

2 Grab a few friends to be your audience. Show the eight of diamonds and the seven of hearts to your audience to prove to them that they're normal cards.

3 Ask someone to place these two cards on the bottom of the deck. Next, tell your audience that you're going to magically make these two cards appear on the top of the deck.

4 Quickly knock three times on the top of the deck and turn up the top two cards. These cards are actually the eight of *hearts* and seven of *diamonds*, which you put there earlier, but your audience will think they're the eight of diamonds and the seven of hearts that were placed on the bottom of the deck. Most people will never notice the switch because the cards look so much alike!

...Y'KNOW, PEOPLE ALWAYS THINK I'M YOU...!

34 MY SHIP SAILS

All on board! This is one card game that will suit anyone—as long as the player collects enough cards of one suit!

WHAT YOU'LL NEED

• three or more players

HOW TO PLAY

1 Choose one person to be the dealer. The dealer shuffles the cards and deals out seven cards, one at a time, face down, to each player. The dealer sets the leftover cards aside.

2 Players pick up their cards and arrange them in a fan shape.

3 The goal of the game is to collect seven cards of the same suit. When the dealer says "go," players in unison take one card they don't want from their hands, lay it face down on the table or floor, and slide it to the player on their left.

4 Players pick up their new cards and put them in their hands, then each chooses another card to pass. Players continue passing cards around the table until one person has all seven cards in the same suit. This person says, "My ship sails!" and lays down his or her cards to show the rest of the players that the game is over!

MY SHIP SAILS!!

ALL IN THE SHUFFLE

This trick is based on a complicated mathematical formula. But it's a breeze to perform, because your audience does all the work!

HOW TO DO IT

1 Tell a friend, "You have the power to be a magician, and I can prove it. In this trick, you will remove one card, bury it in a stack of cards, then find it again!"

2 Next, take ten cards off the top of a deck and give them to your friend. Set the rest of the cards aside— you won't be using them. Tell the friend to shuffle the ten cards and then choose one card, but not to tell you what it is.

3 Tell your friend to count the number of cards from the top of the stack to, and including, the chosen card and remember this number.

4 Take the cards from your friend, saying, "I will cut the deck exactly in half." Push off the top five cards and move them to the bottom. Hand the cards back to your friend.

5 Ask your friend what number he or she remembered from Step 3. Then ask him or her to move that number of cards, one at a time, from the top of the stack to the bottom.

TO PERFORM THE ELIMINATION SHUFFLE, SIMPLY TAKE THE TOP CARD AND PUT IT ON THE BOTTOM--

--THEN TAKE THE NEXT CARD AND PLACE IT ON THE TABLE...

...REPEAT THIS PROCESS UNTIL ONLY ONE CARD IS LEFT IN YOUR HAND.

6 Now ask your friend to perform the "elimination shuffle," and that this will magically reveal his or her chosen card. To do the elimination shuffle, have your friend take the top card and put it at the bottom of the deck. Then take the next card and put it on a table. Take the following card and put it on the bottom of the deck. The next card is placed on the table, and so on.

7 The friend continues the elimination shuffle until only one card is left. Ask your friend to turn over that last card. Guess what? It will be his or her chosen card!

36 ON THE NOSE

The players who win this game will stand out as plain as the noses on their faces!

WHAT YOU'LL NEED

• four to thirteen players

HOW TO PLAY

1 Depending on the number of players, you first need to figure out how many cards will be used. With four players you use only the aces, kings, queens, and jacks. The rest of the cards are set aside. With five players, add the tens. With six players, add the nines; with seven players, add the eights; with eight players, add the sevens; and so on.

2 Choose one person to be the dealer. The dealer shuffles the cards and hands them all out, one at a time, face down, to the players.

3 Players arrange the cards in a fan shape, then by sets. A set is a group of matching cards, such as three jacks or two nines. The object of this game is to collect a book—four cards that match.

4 When the dealer says "go," each player takes a card out of his or her hand and passes it to the player on his or her left. Players add the new cards to their hands, arranging them by number.

5 Continue playing until one person has a book. The first person to collect a book quietly lays a finger on his or her nose. As soon as the other players notice the finger, they should quickly and quietly touch their noses, too. The last person to touch his or her nose is the loser.

STRATEGY ALERT: Don't discard two or more matching cards. Hold onto those cards and try to make a book.

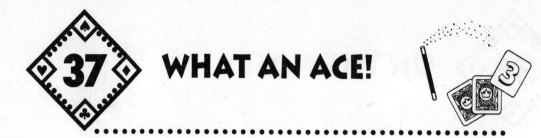

37 WHAT AN ACE!

You'll look oh so impressive when you find an ace without even looking at the deck of cards.

WHAT YOU'LL NEED

• table that you and your friend can reach under

HOW TO DO IT

1 Sit across the table from your friend. While you shuffle the deck of cards, take a peek at the card on the bottom and remember it.

2 Hand the deck, face down, to your friend. Ask your friend to turn the cards face up, fan through them, and find an ace—any ace. Ask the friend to then turn the deck face down again, and place the ace on top of the deck. Also ask him or her to take a look at the bottom card, and to remember it.

3 When your friend is finished, ask him or her to hand you the deck under the table. Grab the deck with your right hand and turn your palm over so the deck is now face up. This reverses the order of the cards. Now the ace is on the bottom.

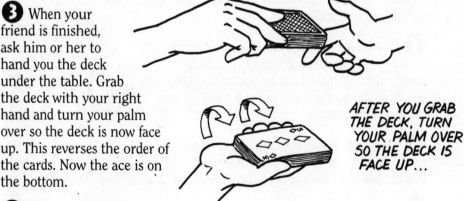

AFTER YOU GRAB THE DECK, TURN YOUR PALM OVER SO THE DECK IS FACE UP...

4 Tell your friend to reach under the table and take the top card. Ask that his or her hands stay *under* the table the whole time. Your friend will think the card is the ace that he or she put on top. But since you turned the cards over, he or she will really be taking the *bottom* card.

5 Both of you keep your hands under the table. Next, tell your friend to place the "ace" into the middle of the deck.

6 Secretly turn your hand over so that the ace is now back on top.

7 Still keep your hands under the table. Ask your friend to take the bottom card off the deck and hand it to you under the table. Say, "This card will help me find your ace." Keep one hand with the cards under the table. Bring the bottom card out and look at it. Say the name of the card you remember seeing on the bottom, out loud. This will *not* be the card you are looking at. Put this card back under the table and onto the bottom of the deck.

8 Rap the bottom of the table with your hand three times. Take the top card off the deck and bring it up to the table. Turn it over and show that it is your friend's ace. Because your friend thought he or she hid the ace in the middle of the deck, your friend will be very impressed that you found it!

9 For the finish, hand your friend the deck of cards and tell him or her to find the original bottom card. Your friend will be amazed to find this card is now in the middle of the deck.

STRATEGY ALERT: The secret to this trick is to remember at all times which way the cards are facing—up or down—while they are under the table.

 **MEMORY MADNESS**

This matching game will not only maximize your memory skills but your fun as well!

WHAT YOU'LL NEED

• two to six players

HOW TO PLAY

1 Choose one person to be the dealer. The dealer pulls a card from the middle of the stack and shows it to all the players. This card, and the others with the same value, are wild cards. This means that they will match with any other card.

2 The dealer next lays all the cards, face down, in front of the other players. He or she can lay the cards out in any design he or she wants.

3 The person to the left of the dealer goes first. He or she turns up any two cards. If they make a pair, the player gets to keep them. The player then gets to try to make another match. If the cards don't make a pair, he or she puts them back, turning them face down. The turn goes to the next player.

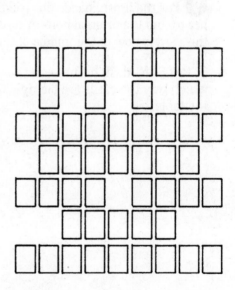

4 Keep taking turns until all the cards have been paired up. And don't forget the wild card. If it turns up with any other card, it is an automatic match! The player with the most pairs is the winner—and has the most impressive memory!

39 POOF, IT'S GONE!

Where, oh, where did the card go? This is one trick your friends will never figure out—unless you come clean with the secret!

WHAT YOU'LL NEED

• bar of soap

RUB DAB OF SOAP ONTO CARD.

HOW TO DO IT

1 Before you perform this trick, rub a pea-sized dab of soap on the tip of your thumb.

2 Line up your audience on the other side of a small table. Allow one person to shuffle the deck of cards and return it to you.

3 Pick up the top card. Hold it so that your thumb is in the center of the face of the card. While showing it to your audience, rub the dab of soap onto the center of the card.

4 Lay this card face down on the top of the deck and make all the edges even. Tell your audience that you are going to press this card into the middle of the deck and make it disappear. Press hard on top of the deck. (This sets the dab of soap, causing the top two cards to stick together.)

PRESS HARD ON TOP OF THE DECK TO ENSURE THE CARDS STICK...

5 Pick up the top card and show it to the audience. This will be a different card than the one you started with because the top card is now stuck to the second card! No one will ever guess your secret!

40 BULL'S-EYE

Gather up a group and see who's the best shot.

WHAT YOU'LL NEED

• two to thirteen players
• large hat
• ruler

HOW TO PLAY

1 Give each player four cards that match. For example, one player gets four sevens, another player gets four twos, the next player gets four tens, and so on.

2 Arrange everyone around the room in a giant circle. Place the hat in the middle of the circle.

3 Go around the circle, giving everyone a chance to flip his or her cards into the hat.

4 Use the ruler to measure how close each toss is to the hat. Award players the following points:

    more than 12 inches from the hat .... 0 points
    under 12 inches, more than 6 inches ...... 5 points
    under 6 inches, more than 2 inches ....10 points
    under 2 inches...15 points
    Bull's-eye..25 points

Add up the points and give a prize—maybe a new hat—to the player with the highest score.

41 KING'S COURT

Your friends will be amazed at your power to place four kings randomly into a deck of cards and then bring them together.

HOW TO DO IT

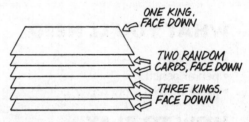

ONE KING, FACE DOWN

TWO RANDOM CARDS, FACE DOWN

THREE KINGS, FACE DOWN

1 Before performing the trick you need to arrange the cards in a certain order when no one is looking. First, remove the four kings from the deck and set the rest of the deck aside—you'll use it later. Place three kings face down on the table on top of each other. Place *any* two other cards face down on top of the kings. Then place the fourth king on the top, face down. Fan the kings face up so that the two extra cards in the middle are hidden from the audience.

2 Now that your kings are arranged, call in your audience. Show the four kings to the audience. Next say, "Now I'm going to place three of these kings randomly into the deck." Put your "kings" selection on top of the deck, face down.

3 Pick up the top card (a king) and place it on the very bottom of the deck. Pick up the second card (not a king) and place it anywhere in the lower half of the deck. Pick up the third card (not a king) and place it anywhere in the upper half of the deck. Now there will be one king on the bottom and three still on top.

TWO HIDDEN CARDS

4 Pick up the top half of the cards and set it to your right. Then pick up the bottom half of the cards and place it on top of the stack. The four kings are now together in the middle of the deck.

5 Now tell your audience, "I will bring the kings back together." Tap gently four times on the deck. Turn the deck face up and fan through the cards until you find all four kings, lined up together, in the middle of the deck. How did you do it? As long as the kings don't talk, your friends will never know!

42 TWO-PERSON RUMMY

This game is one long run to the finish to see which player is the first to have a hand filled with all sets or runs.

WHAT YOU'LL NEED

- two players
- pen or pencil
- paper to keep score on

HOW TO PLAY

1 Choose one person to be the dealer. The dealer shuffles the cards and deals each player ten cards, one at a time, face down. The dealer places the leftover cards face down in the middle of the circle. This is the pickup pile. The dealer turns up the top card on the pickup pile and sets it down, face up, to create a second pile. This is the throw-away pile.

2 Players arrange their hands in a fan shape. Then they arrange their hands in runs or sets. A run is a series of three or more cards in the same suit in numerical order, such as the five, six, and seven of diamonds. A set is three or four cards that are the same number, such as four nines. The first player to have his or her hand filled completely with runs or sets "goes out" and wins the game.

A "RUN" CONSISTS OF THREE OR MORE CARDS OF THE SAME SUIT, IN NUMERICAL ORDER...

3 The player who didn't deal goes first and gets a chance to choose a new card to help complete a run or set. He or she has the choice of taking a card from the pickup pile or from the throw-away pile. After picking up the new card, the player discards a card from his or her hand onto the throw-away pile, face up.

4 The second player then chooses and discards a card. Players take turns until one player's hand is filled with all the cards in sets or runs. The winning player discards the final card face down on the throw-away pile, then lays down all of the cards, displaying the runs and sets. This is called "rummy."

5 The first person to rummy gets points from the other player's cards. Any cards that do not make up a complete run or a complete set will count as points. The points are:

aces..11 points
kings, queens, jacks ....10 points
all other cards ....numeric value

6 Add up all the points and keep score. Play as many games as you can or until one person makes 100 points. The first person to get 100 points is the grand winner!

A "SET" CONSISTS OF THREE OR FOUR CARDS THAT ARE THE SAME NUMBER...

TO MAKE IT TOUGHER: Alternate games. In one game, make only runs allowable. In the next game, make only sets allowable.

43 BLIND MAN'S POKER

In this goofy game you get to look at your opponent's card and NOT your own!

WHAT YOU'LL NEED

- two players
- pen and paper for keeping score

HOW TO PLAY

1 Players sit across from each other. One person is the dealer. He or she shuffles the cards and deals out one card to each player, face down. Players do not look at their cards.

2 When the dealer says "go," both players pick up their cards at the same time and hold them to their foreheads, face out, toward the other player. Now they can see the other player's card but not their own.

3 The player who is not the dealer goes first and guesses if his or her card is higher than the other person's card. Then the second player makes a guess as to whose card is higher.

4 Both players then lay their cards down and see if they were right.

5 Each player gets 10 points for a correct guess, plus the points of their card. The points for cards are:

aces ....15 points
kings, queens, jacks ....10 points
all other cards..numeric value

After the first round, the next person deals.

6 Keep playing until one person wins 100 points.

44 ◆ CLASH

This variation of the game of War makes for a fun face-off with a friend.

WHAT YOU'LL NEED

• two players

HOW TO PLAY

1 Choose one person to be the dealer. The dealer draws one card out of the middle of the stack and shows it to the other player. This card and the others with the same value—for example, all sixes or all jacks—will be wild for this game. The wild card beats any other card.

2 The dealer shuffles the cards and deals out the entire deck, one at a time, face down, into two stacks, one stack for each player. Players pick up their stacks, but do not look at them.

3 Both players turn up their top cards at the same time in the middle of the playing area. The person with the highest card wins both the cards—unless it's a wild card, which is the automatic winner. The player with the high card collects the cards in the middle and places them, face down, under his or her stack.

4 Players continue turning over cards and winning sets of cards.

5 The real fun comes when players turn over cards that match, such as two tens or two queens. This is the "clash" you've been waiting for. To settle the dispute, both players place three cards, face down, next to their clash card. Then both players turn up a fourth card. The person with the highest fourth card wins all the cards in the middle. (And if the two cards turned over at this point match, place three more cards face down and face off again!)

6 Keep playing until one person has all the cards. Or, if you're exhausted from battle and want to end the game early, count up your cards. The person with the most cards is the winner.

TO MAKE IT TOUGHER: After three "clashes" in one game, the dealer can pick another wild card from an extra deck of cards so there are two types of wild cards to look out for.

45 SIX AND THREE-QUARTERS

This cute magic trick will not only wow your audience, it also comes with a built-in play on words.

WHAT YOU'LL NEED

• deck of cards with jokers

HOW TO DO IT

TEAR OFF BOTTOM QUARTER

1 First, you'll need to prepare the deck when no one is looking. To start, pull out the two of clubs and set it aside. Then, tear off the bottom quarter of the joker. Place this joker on the table, face down. Count any six cards from the top of the deck, face down, and cover the joker. Finally, place the two of clubs on top of the six cards, face up. Place the rest of the deck face down on top of the two of clubs. Now you're ready to perform the trick.

2 Grab a friend to be your audience. Fan the cards out in front of your friend and ask him or her to select a card from the middle of the deck, remember it, then replace it on top of the deck, face down. Tell your friend, "Now I am going to find your card."

3 Take the cards and cut them. This puts the chosen card underneath your joker, which will help you find it. Tell your friend that first you are going to look for the two of clubs, because it will help you find the card he or she selected.

4 Flip through the cards until you come to the two of clubs, which is easy to find because it is face up. While you show this card to your friend, move the cards that came before the two of clubs to the bottom of the deck face down. Lay the two of clubs aside—you don't need it anymore.

5 Now you're ready to find the card—and make a play on words at the same time—based on the way you've set up the deck. Tell your friend, "According to my calculations, your card is exactly six and three-quarters down from the top!"

← FACE UP, TWO OF CLUBS

↙ SIX CARDS, FACE DOWN

↖ TORN JOKER, FACE DOWN

6 Your friend won't know what you mean yet, but that's okay. Slowly, dramatically deal cards off the top, counting as you go: "One . . . two . . ." and so on, until you count six. The next card is the joker. Pick it up and show that it is only three-quarters of a card, then say, ". . . and three-quarters. That means your card is right here!"

7 Pick up the next card on the stack, turning it up to show it is the card he or she picked at the very beginning!

 **BOWLING SOLITAIRE**

You don't need to go to the bowling alley to play this game that will really knock you over!

HOW TO PLAY

1 Remove all the aces, kings, queens, jacks, and tens from the deck. This will give you twenty cards. Set the rest of the deck aside— you won't be needing it.

J	Q	A	K

J	A	Q

Q	10

K

2 Shuffle the twenty cards and then lay out the first ten, *face up*, in bowling pin layout.

3 The other cards are your "ball" cards. Turn over a ball card. If it matches a bowling pin card, remove the pin card from the layout and place it in front of you.

4 Keep turning over ball cards and removing pin cards. If you remove all the pin cards before you run out of ball cards, you win.

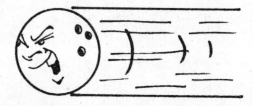

47 ABOUT FACE

This easy but entertaining trick works due to the fact that the deck mixes both face-up and face-down cards.

HOW TO DO IT

1 Give a friend a deck of cards and ask him or her to cut the cards into three nearly equal piles. The exact number of cards in each pile doesn't matter.

2 Next, ask your friend to pick up one pile and shuffle it. Then ask him or her to look at the top card on this pile and remember it.

3 Ask your friend to place this pile FACE UP on top of either of the two FACE-DOWN piles. The remaining pile should be placed FACE DOWN on top of this stack. The deck will now have both FACE-UP and FACE-DOWN cards.

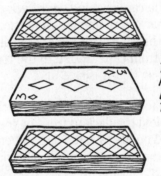

THE FACE-UP PILE SHOULD BE IN BETWEEN THE FACE-DOWN PILES...

4 For the next step, ask your friend to cut the deck, shuffle the cards, then give you back the deck. Say, "Now I will find the card you chose."

5 Turn the deck FACE UP and fan through the cards until you come to the first long string of FACE-UP cards. Fan past these cards to the very next FACE-DOWN card. Turn this card up, and it will be the card your friend noted in the beginning.

48 DON'T LOOK BACK!

This trick is so simple, you can find a chosen card with both hands behind your back. The challenge is fooling your audience into thinking the trick is harder than it really is!

HOW TO DO IT

1 Fan out the deck of cards and offer them, face down, to someone in your audience. Ask him or her to pick a card and not to let you see what it is.

2 Put the cards back into a single deck and ask that person to place the chosen card on the bottom of the deck.

3 Take the cards behind your back and tell your audience that you're going to find the selected card by mixing up the cards. But instead of mixing up the cards, slide the bottom card around to the top of the deck and turn it over so that it is face up.

4 After a few seconds, bring the deck around to the front. Hold the deck in front of you so that the *bottom* card points toward your audience. The card facing you (on top) is the card your friend picked. Remember it.

WHILE THE DECK IS BEHIND YOUR BACK, SLIDE THE CHOSEN CARD AROUND FROM BOTTOM TO THE TOP.

5 The hard part of the trick is over for you, because you already know which card your friend selected. The rest of the trick is to fool your audience into thinking that the trick is a lot harder than it actually is, so they'll be more impressed with your magic skills. To do this, ask the audience if the bottom card you're showing is the chosen card. The audience will groan and say no. You can reply, "Just kidding, folks!"

6 Next, tell your audience that you're going to mix up the cards behind your back one more time and try again to find the chosen card. But instead of mixing up the cards, turn the selected card over so the back is showing like the others, and slide it back into the deck.

YOUR AUDIENCE SEES
THE BOTTOM CARD;
YOU SEE THE CHOSEN
CARD...

7 Bring the deck around to the front. Tell your audience that you're going to look for the chosen card. Begin to turn over cards, studying each one for a second as if it might be the chosen card.

8 While you are turning over cards, you will pass the chosen card. Don't let on that you know it's the chosen card—keep the suspense building for a few more minutes. Your audience will probably groan or giggle and think you've really blown the trick.

9 Turn over a few more cards, then announce, "The next card I turn over will be the chosen card." Everyone will probably burst out laughing because they know you've already passed the card. With a straight face, reach down into the cards you've already turned over and find the chosen card. Show it to your audience, then turn it over face down and say, "Here it is!" Your audience will be shocked and surprised that you pulled this one off!

49 CAPTURE THE CARD

Be the general of your own army of cards and try to take the most "prisoners" from your opponent's hands.

WHAT YOU'LL NEED

• two players

HOW TO PLAY

1 Players sit across from each other at a table or on the floor.

2 Choose one person to be the dealer. The dealer shuffles the cards and deals them all out, one at a time, face down, in two stacks, one for each player.

3 Players pick up their stacks but don't look at their cards.

4 The player who didn't deal begins the game by turning the top card face up and placing it in the center playing area. The dealer then turns his or her top card face up, and places it head-to-head with the first card.

5 If the cards are number cards (ten, nine, eight, seven, six, five, four, three, or two), each player turns up another card. Continue playing until one person turns over an ace or a face card.

6 The first player to turn up an ace or a face card says, "Prepare to be my prisoner." The second player answers, "Not if I can help it!" He or she then turns up from *one to four cards*, hoping to find an ace or face card higher than the first player's card. If he or she doesn't turn over a higher card, the first player takes all the cards in the center playing area as his or her "prisoners." But, if the second player is lucky and

turns up a higher card, he or she announces, "Now prepare to be *my* prisoner!" The first player is now under attack. He or she can turn over as many as four cards to try to find an even higher card. If he or she can't, the second player wins all the cards in the center playing area. If at any point there is a tie, both players turn over a card, and that highest card determines the winner for that round.

7 Players return to their stacks and begin again, turning up one card at a time. Continue to "battle" for cards each time an ace or face card is turned up. If at any time both players turn up the same card, such as two kings, they each turn up as many cards as it takes until one turns up a higher card.

8 The player who finally runs out of cards loses, and the game is over.

9 If you run out of time and have to stop playing before one person has captured all the cards, have each player count his or her captured cards. The person with the most cards wins the game—and the war!

 **GO FOR IT!**

You'll probably get your friends to go for this silly game only once. So get a group together and give it your best shot!

HOW TO PLAY

1 Gather your friends into a circle and tell them, "You are about to play the most incredible, amazing, unbelievable card game in the history of mankind. It's called Go for It."

2 Hold all the cards in one hand and throw them in the air.

3 While your friends look at you, wondering what kind of game this is, tell them, "Go for it."

4 Explain that the trick is that they have to "go for" all the cards and pick them up. You can expect a few grumbles, but most of your pals will no doubt grin and bear it and pick up all the cards.